Contents

2-3
Instructions

4 – 43
Exercises

÷

44-47
Best Set Graphs

+

48
Animate Antonio

—

49
Prizes

About The Book

This book is designed for children learning to count. As adults we forget what it means to learn to count — we forget quite how baffling the concept of numbers can be.
I developed the concepts behind this book over the course of several years, teaching various underperforming five to six year olds how to get on top of numbers between 1 and 10.

These exercises are designed to facilitate what is commonly practiced at primary schools, namely 'Number Bonds.' The system in the book is an adapted version of the ANT Maths Training series. It utilises the same principles – goal and reward focused exercises, presented on a beautiful, symmetrical template, which children enjoy working on, and coming back to.

There are four different types of exercise, A, B, C and Medley. Each exercise requires the child to complete a different part of a question – rather than only the answer – and thus builds a complete numerical framework within their brain. Furthermore, answers are written on the letter 'x' which introduces from an early age the idea that a letter can be a number – the basis of algebra.

The exercises are enjoyable, as long as the student has the methodology to tackle them. With that in mind it is fundamental that students are not timed if they are unconfident. Before attempting these exercises, the student should be able to use their fingers to count to ten forwards and backwards, and be able to work out, on their fingers, how many they need to get to ten.

Until they are confident enough to do this, you should allow them to do the exercises untimed and reward them with Bronze medals, simply for completing the task. Help them learn how to use their fingers as reference points.

Once you see that they are taking around 90 seconds to complete – you don't need to formally time – you can begin to introduce the timing element, and start asking them to set goals.

It is paramount that goal setting, prize giving, and graph plotting take place. This process embeds the principal that practice equals improvement, and will give your child a healthy work ethic, based on self-belief. Make sure you show them the graph frequently, to remind them of the fruits of their labours, and instil the belief that their destiny is in their own hands.

Used with patience and persistence, this book will help your child build a solid and lasting foundation on which to base their entire mathematical construct.

Alexander F.L. Newberry
MSt. Oxon FRSA
ANT Founder

Instructions

1) Instruct child to fill in the date. If they don't, they won't be eligible for their 1 second exercise bonus.

2) Instruct them to set their goal. Allow them to set whatever goal they like. They must set a goal to get a bonus.

3) As long as they are confident, time them completing the exercise. (see 'About The Book')

4) Once they have finished, stop the clock and ask them to check their work for mistakes. (Such as writing numbers the wrong way round.)

5) Once they have checked, write their time down, and reward them with their 2 second bonus, and whatever ANT prize they have won. Make a show of the prize giving to make them feel good.

6) If they have achieved their goal or set a Personal Best, they can stick a Goal/PB sticker onto Antonio's eyes, thus making Antonio's face complete. You should encourage them to do this.

7) Plot their time on the graph in the back of the book. If they have taken more than a minute you must convert their time into seconds. You can explain to them what you are doing – see if they can understand the concept that 60 seconds = 1 minute.

8) Young children learning to count usually have short attention spans. They will probably only manage 1 exercise at a time, but if they are keen to try more, let them.

9) Never force the issue. Be patient. If they don't want to do it, they lack confidence. Use finger counting to ground them in something tangible, then try again.

copyright ant.london

Date	Number Bonds To Ten	Ex.	1

Circle your goal. Fill in the numbers in the 'A' Column. If you write the date and get 100% you get a 2 second bonus!

Medals & Prizes!

Make Antonio by setting a Personal Best, reaching your goal, and winning a medal.

ANT	20
Gold	30
Silver	50
Bronze	1:30
Hand Speed	
Bonus	
Total Time	

ANTONIO
P * B   GOAL

Question	A		B		C
1	x	+	1	=	10
2	x	+	0	=	10
3	x	+	3	=	10
4	x	+	6	=	10
5	x	+	10	=	10
6	x	+	8	=	10
7	x	+	8	=	10
8	x	+	7	=	10
9	x	+	6	=	10
10	x	+	8	=	10

copyright ant.london

| Ex. | 2 | Number Bonds To Ten | Date |

Circle your goal. Fill in the numbers in the 'B' Column. If you write the date and get 100% you get a 2 second bonus!

Question	A		B		C	Medals & Prizes!
1	10	+	x	=	10	Make Antonio by setting a Personal Best, reaching your goal, and winning a medal.
2	10	+	x	=	10	20 — ANT
3	4	+	x	=	10	30 — Gold
4	0	+	x	=	10	50 — Silver
5	7	+	x	=	10	1:30 — Bronze
6	6	+	x	=	10	Hand Speed / Bonus / Total Time
7	3	+	x	=	10	ANTONIO
8	2	+	x	=	10	P * B — GOAL
9	10	+	x	=	10	
10	1	+	x	=	10	

copyright ant.london

Date	Number Bonds To Ten - C Type	Ex	3

Circle your goal. Fill in the numbers in the 'C' Column. Check your answers. If you write the date and get 100% you get a 2 second bonus!

Medals & Prizes!

Make Antonio by setting a Personal Best, reaching your goal, and winning a medal.

ANT	20
Gold	30
Silver	50
Bronze	1:30

Hand Speed
Bonus
Total Time

ANTONIO
P * B   GOAL

Question	A		B		C
1	2	+	4	=	x
2	0	+	9	=	x
3	2	+	3	=	x
4	2	+	0	=	x
5	5	+	3	=	x
6	2	+	6	=	x
7	4	+	4	=	x
8	2	+	3	=	x
9	2	+	5	=	x
10	3	+	0	=	x

copyright ant.london

| Ex. | 4 | Number Bonds To Ten - Medley | Date |

Circle your goal. Fill in the numbers in the boxes marked 'X'. Check your answers. If you write the date and get 100% you get a 2 second bonus!

Question	A		B		C	Medals & Prizes!	
1	X	+	0	=	10	Make Antonio by setting a Personal Best, reaching your goal, and winning a medal.	
2	5	+	X	=	10	20	ANT
3	4	+	2	=	X	30	Gold
4	6	+	X	=	10	50	Silver
5	X	+	0	=	10	1:30	Bronze
6	9	+	X	=	10		Hand Speed
7	4	+	1	=	X		Bonus
8	4	+	X	=	10		Total Time
9	X	+	3	=	10	ANTONIO P * B	GOAL
10	9	+	X	=	10		

copyright ant.london

Date	Number Bonds To Ten - A Type	Ex.	5

Circle your goal. Fill in the numbers in the 'A' Column. If you write the date and get 100% you get a 2 second bonus!

Medals & Prizes!

Make Antonio by setting a Personal Best, reaching your goal, and winning a medal.

ANT	20
Gold	30
Silver	50
Bronze	1:30

Hand Speed
Bonus
Total Time

ANTONIO
P * B   GOAL

Question	A		B		C
1	x	+	6	=	10
2	x	+	9	=	10
3	x	+	3	=	10
4	x	+	10	=	10
5	x	+	8	=	10
6	x	+	4	=	10
7	x	+	7	=	10
8	x	+	1	=	10
9	x	+	10	=	10
10	x	+	7	=	10

copyright ant.london

| Ex. | 6 | Number Bonds To Ten - B Type | Date |

Circle your goal. Fill in the numbers in the 'B' Column. If you write the date and get 100% you get a 2 second bonus!

Question	A		B		C	Medals & Prizes!	
1	10	+		=	10	Make Antonio by setting a Personal Best, reaching your goal, and winning a medal.	
2	3	+		=	10	20	ANT
3	2	+		=	10	30	Gold
4	6	+		=	10	50	Silver
5	5	+		=	10	1:30	Bronze
6	9	+		=	10		Hand Speed
							Bonus
							Total Time
7	0	+		=	10	ANTONIO	
						P * B	GOAL
8	0	+		=	10		
9	3	+		=	10		
10	1	+		=	10		

copyright ant.london

Date	Number Bonds To Ten - C Type	Ex	7

Circle your goal. Fill in the numbers in the 'C' Column. Check your answers. If you write the date and get 100% you get a 2 second bonus!

Medals & Prizes!

Make Antonio by setting a Personal Best, reaching your goal, and winning a medal.

Medal	Time
ANT	20
Gold	30
Silver	50
Bronze	1:30

Hand Speed
Bonus
Total Time

ANTONIO
P * B   GOAL

Question	A		B		C
1	2	+	2	=	x
2	1	+	9	=	x
3	3	+	5	=	x
4	4	+	0	=	x
5	4	+	4	=	x
6	1	+	7	=	x
7	0	+	3	=	x
8	2	+	1	=	x
9	4	+	2	=	x
10	5	+	1	=	x

copyright ant.london

Ex.	8	Number Bonds To Ten - Medley		Date	

Circle your goal. Fill in the numbers iin the boxes marked 'X'. Check your answers. If you write the date and get 100% you get a 2 second bonus!

Question	A		B		C	Medals & Prizes!	
1	X	+	0	=	10	Make Antonio by setting a Personal Best, reaching your goal, and winning a medal.	
2	4	+	X	=	10	20	ANT
3	3	+	3	=	X	30	Gold
4	0	+	X	=	10	50	Silver
5	X	+	9	=	10	1:30	Bronze
6	5	+	X	=	10		Hand Speed
							Bonus
7	0	+	5	=	X		Total Time
8	3	+	X	=	10	ANTONIO P*B GOAL	
9	X	+	10	=	10		
10	3	+	X	=	10		

copyright ant.london

Date	Number Bonds To Ten - A Type	Ex.	9

Circle your goal. Fill in the numbers in the 'A' Column. If you write the date and get 100% you get a 2 second bonus!

Medals & Prizes!

Make Antonio by setting a Personal Best, reaching your goal, and winning a medal.

Medal	Time
ANT	20
Gold	30
Silver	50
Bronze	1:30

Hand Speed
Bonus
Total Time

ANTONIO
P*B   GOAL

Question	A		B		C
1	x	+	8	=	10
2	x	+	0	=	10
3	x	+	6	=	10
4	x	+	8	=	10
5	x	+	4	=	10
6	x	+	9	=	10
7	x	+	6	=	10
8	x	+	2	=	10
9	x	+	3	=	10
10	x	+	5	=	10

copyright ant.london

Ex.	10	Number Bonds To Ten - B Type	Date

Circle your goal. Fill in the numbers in the 'B' Column. If you write the date and get 100% you get a 2 second bonus!

Question	A		B		C	Medals & Prizes!	
1	10	+		=	10	Make Antonio by setting a Personal Best, reaching your goal, and winning a medal.	
2	10	+		=	10	20	ANT
3	7	+		=	10	30	Gold
4	8	+		=	10	50	Silver
5	2	+		=	10	1:30	Bronze
6	4	+		=	10	Hand Speed	
						Bonus	
7	6	+		=	10	Total Time	
						ANTONIO	
						P * B	GOAL
8	3	+		=	10		
9	4	+		=	10		
10	6	+		=	10		

copyright ant.london

| | | Date | | Number Bonds To Ten - C Type | | | | Ex | 11 |

Circle your goal. Fill in the numbers in the 'C' Column. Check your answers. If you write the date and get 100% you get a 2 second bonus!

Medals & Prizes!

Make Antonio by setting a Personal Best, reaching your goal, and winning a medal.

Medal	Time
ANT	20
Gold	30
Silver	50
Bronze	1:30

Hand Speed
Bonus
Total Time

ANTONIO
P * B   GOAL

Question	A		B		C
1	4	+	4	=	x
2	1	+	9	=	x
3	2	+	5	=	x
4	4	+	4	=	x
5	2	+	2	=	x
6	1	+	5	=	x
7	3	+	3	=	x
8	4	+	4	=	x
9	4	+	3	=	x
10	2	+	5	=	x

copyright ant.london

Ex.	12	Number Bonds To Ten - Medley	Date

Circle your goal. Fill in the numbers iin the boxes marked 'X'. Check your answers. If you write the date and get 100% you get a 2 second bonus!

Question	A		B		C	Medals & Prizes!
1	X	+	5	=	10	Make Antonio by setting a Personal Best, reaching your goal, and winning a medal.
2	4	+	X	=	10	20 — ANT
3	1	+	3	=	X	30 — Gold
4	7	+	X	=	10	50 — Silver
5	X	+	6	=	10	1:30 — Bronze
6	2	+	X	=	10	Hand Speed / Bonus / Total Time
7	2	+	1	=	X	ANTONIO P*B GOAL
8	4	+	X	=	10	
9	X	+	7	=	10	
10	7	+	X	=	10	

ant.london

Date	Number Bonds To Ten - A Type	Ex.	13

Circle your goal. Fill in the numbers in the 'A' Column. If you write the date and get 100% you get a 2 second bonus!

Medals & Prizes!

Make Antonio by setting a Personal Best, reaching your goal, and winning a medal.

ANT	20
Gold	30
Silver	50
Bronze	1:30
Hand Speed	
Bonus	
Total Time	

ANTONIO
P * B   GOAL

Question	A		B		C
1	x	+	10	=	10
2	x	+	8	=	10
3	x	+	1	=	10
4	x	+	3	=	10
5	x	+	0	=	10
6	x	+	10	=	10
7	x	+	4	=	10
8	x	+	4	=	10
9	x	+	10	=	10
10	x	+	6	=	10

copyright ant.london

Ex.	14	Number Bonds To Ten - B Type	Date

Circle your goal. Fill in the numbers in the 'B' Column. If you write the date and get 100% you get a 2 second bonus!

Question	A		B		C	Medals & Prizes!	
1	3	+		=	10	Make Antonio by setting a Personal Best, reaching your goal, and winning a medal.	
2	10	+		=	10	20	ANT
3	9	+		=	10	30	Gold
4	0	+		=	10	50	Silver
5	7	+		=	10	1:30	Bronze
6	9	+		=	10		Hand Speed
							Bonus
7	0	+		=	10		Total Time
8	2	+		=	10	ANTONIO P * B — GOAL	
9	1	+		=	10		
10	10	+		=	10		

copyright ant.london

Number Bonds To Ten - C Type

Ex 15

Circle your goal. Fill in the numbers in the 'C' Column. Check your answers. If you write the date and get 100% you get a 2 second bonus!

Medals & Prizes!

Make Antonio by setting a Personal Best, reaching your goal, and winning a medal.

ANT	20
Gold	30
Silver	50
Bronze	1:30

Hand Speed
Bonus
Total Time

ANTONIO
P * B   GOAL

Question	A		B		C
1	4	+	2	=	6
2	1	+	9	=	10
3	3	+	4	=	7
4	0	+	0	=	0
5	5	+	5	=	10
6	1	+	6	=	7
7	4	+	3	=	7
8	0	+	2	=	2
9	5	+	2	=	7
10	2	+	2	=	4

Ex.	16	Number Bonds To Ten - Medley

Circle your goal. Fill in the numbers in the boxes marked 'X'. Check your answers. If you write the date and get 100% you get a 2 second bonus!

Question	A		B		C	Medals & Prizes!
1	9	+	1	=	10	Make Antonio by setting a Personal Best, reaching your goal, and winning a medal.
2	7	+	3	=	10	20 — ANT
3	1	+	5	=	6	30 — Gold
4	5	+	5	=	10	50 — Silver
5	8	+	2	=	10	1:30 — Bronze
6	7	+	3	=	10	Hand Speed Bonus
7	3	+	5	=	8	Total Time
8	7	+	3	=	10	ANTONIO — P*B — GOAL
9	7	+	3	=	10	
10	10	+	0	=	10	

copyright ant.london

Date	Number Bonds To Ten - A Type	Ex.	17

Circle your goal. Fill in the numbers in the 'A' Column. If you write the date and get 100% you get a 2 second bonus!

Medals & Prizes!

Make Antonio by setting a Personal Best, reaching your goal, and winning a medal.

ANT	20
Gold	30
Silver	50
Bronze	1:30

Hand Speed
Bonus
Total Time

ANTONIO
P * B — GOAL

Question	A		B		C
1	x	+	10	=	10
2	x	+	3	=	10
3	x	+	5	=	10
4	x	+	5	=	10
5	x	+	10	=	10
6	x	+	5	=	10
7	x	+	0	=	10
8	x	+	10	=	10
9	x	+	0	=	10
10	x	+	0	=	10

copyright ant.london

Ex.	18	Number Bonds To Ten - B Type	Date

Circle your goal. Fill in the numbers in the 'B' Column. If you write the date and get 100% you get a 2 second bonus!

Question	A		B		C	Medals & Prizes!	
1	2	+		=	10	Make Antonio by setting a Personal Best, reaching your goal, and winning a medal.	
2	6	+		=	10	20	ANT
3	1	+		=	10	30	Gold
4	1	+		=	10	50	Silver
5	1	+		=	10	1:30	Bronze
6	2	+		=	10	Hand Speed	
						Bonus	
7	6	+		=	10	Total Time	
8	6	+		=	10	ANTONIO P * B GOAL	
9	2	+		=	10		
10	6	+		=	10		

Date	Number Bonds To Ten - C Type	Ex	19

Circle your goal. Fill in the numbers in the 'C' Column. Check your answers. If you write the date and get 100% you get a 2 second bonus!

Medals & Prizes!

Make Antonio by setting a Personal Best, reaching your goal, and winning a medal.

- ANT — 20
- Gold — 30
- Silver — 50
- Bronze — 1:30

Hand Speed

Bonus

Total Time

ANTONIO

P * B   GOAL

Question	A		B		C
1	2	+	2	=	x
2	1	+	9	=	x
3	5	+	4	=	x
4	5	+	3	=	x
5	5	+	4	=	x
6	1	+	5	=	x
7	3	+	5	=	x
8	4	+	2	=	x
9	3	+	5	=	x
10	2	+	4	=	x

copyright ant.london

| | Ex. | 20 | Number Bonds To Ten - Medley | | | Date |

Circle your goal. Fill in the numbers iin the boxes marked 'X'. Check your answers. If you write the date and get 100% you get a 2 second bonus!

Question	A		B		C	Medals & Prizes!
1	X	+	9	=	10	Make Antonio by setting a Personal Best, reaching your goal, and winning a medal.
2	5	+	X	=	10	20 — ANT
3	2	+	5	=	X	30 — Gold
4	3	+	X	=	10	50 — Silver
5	X	+	4	=	10	1:30 — Bronze
6	6	+	X	=	10	Hand Speed / Bonus / Total Time
7	2	+	1	=	X	ANTONIO P * B GOAL
8	4	+	X	=	10	
9	X	+	10	=	10	
10	9	+	X	=	10	

copyright ant.london

| Date (to qualify for bonus) | Number Bonds To Ten - A Type | Ex. | 21 |

Circle your goal. Fill in the numbers in the 'A' Column. If you write the date and get 100% you get a 2 second bonus!

Medals & Prizes!

Make Antonio by setting a Personal Best, reaching your goal, and winning a medal.

ANT	20
Gold	30
Silver	50
Bronze	1:30

Hand Speed
Bonus
Total Time

ANTONIO
P * B   GOAL

Question	A		B		C
1	x	+	2	=	10
2	x	+	6	=	10
3	x	+	1	=	10
4	x	+	9	=	10
5	x	+	2	=	10
6	x	+	4	=	10
7	x	+	0	=	10
8	x	+	8	=	10
9	x	+	1	=	10
10	x	+	4	=	10

copyright ant.london

Ex.	22	Number Bonds To Ten - B Type	Date

Circle your goal. Fill in the numbers in the 'B' Column. If you write the date and get 100% you get a 2 second bonus!

Question	A		B		C	Medals & Prizes!	
1	9	+		=	10		
2	2	+		=	10	20	ANT
3	2	+		=	10	30	Gold
4	1	+		=	10	50	Silver
5	2	+		=	10	1:30	Bronze
6	3	+		=	10		Hand Speed
7	4	+		=	10		Bonus
8	1	+		=	10		Total Time
9	4	+		=	10	P * B	ANTONIO GOAL
10	3	+		=	10		

copyright ant.london

Number Bonds To Ten - C Type

Ex 23

Circle your goal. Fill in the numbers in the 'C' Column. Check your answers. If you write the date and get 100% you get a 2 second bonus!

Medals & Prizes!

Make Antonio by setting a Personal Best, reaching your goal, and winning a medal.

ANT	20
Gold	30
Silver	50
Bronze	1:30

Hand Speed
Bonus
Total Time

ANTONIO
P * B   GOAL

Question	A		B		C
1	4	+	5	=	9
2	1	+	9	=	10
3	5	+	4	=	9
4	3	+	0	=	3
5	2	+	5	=	7
6	0	+	7	=	7
7	1	+	3	=	4
8	1	+	5	=	6
9	5	+	4	=	9
10	3	+	2	=	5

copyright ant.london

Ex. 24 — Number Bonds To Ten - Medley

Date

Circle your goal. Fill in the numbers in the boxes marked 'X'. Check your answers. If you write the date and get 100% you get a 2 second bonus!

Question	A		B		C
1	0	+	10	=	10
2	9	+	1	=	10
3	2	+	4	=	6
4	9	+	1	=	10
5	6	+	4	=	10
6	1	+	9	=	10
7	2	+	3	=	5
8	4	+	6	=	10
9	5	+	5	=	10
10	1	+	9	=	10

Medals & Prizes!

Make Antonio by setting a Personal Best, reaching your goal, and winning a medal.

20	ANT
30	Gold
50	Silver
1:30	Bronze

Hand Speed Bonus

Total Time

ANTONIO

P * B   GOAL

copyright ant.london

| Date | Number Bonds To Ten - A Type | Ex. | 25 |

Circle your goal. Fill in the numbers in the 'A' Column. If you write the date and get 100% you get a 2 second bonus!

Medals & Prizes!

Make Antonio by setting a Personal Best, reaching your goal, and winning a medal.

Medal	Time
ANT	20
Gold	30
Silver	50
Bronze	1:30

Hand Speed
Bonus
Total Time

ANTONIO
P * B   GOAL

Question	A		B		C
1	x	+	4	=	10
2	x	+	7	=	10
3	x	+	7	=	10
4	x	+	6	=	10
5	x	+	1	=	10
6	x	+	6	=	10
7	x	+	8	=	10
8	x	+	9	=	10
9	x	+	4	=	10
10	x	+	3	=	10

copyright ant.london

Ex.	26	Number Bonds To Ten - B Type	Date

Circle your goal. Fill in the numbers in the 'B' Column. If you write the date and get 100% you get a 2 second bonus!

Question	A		B		C	Medals & Prizes!	
1	4	+		=	10	Make Antonio by setting a Personal Best, reaching your goal, and winning a medal.	
2	2	+		=	10	20	ANT
3	1	+		=	10	30	Gold
4	1	+		=	10	50	Silver
5	7	+		=	10	1:30	Bronze
6	9	+		=	10	Hand Speed	
						Bonus	
7	10	+		=	10	Total Time	
8	6	+		=	10	ANTONIO P * B GOAL	
9	2	+		=	10		
10	2	+		=	10		

copyright ant.london

Date	Number Bonds To Ten - C Type	Ex	27

Circle your goal. Fill in the numbers in the 'C' Column. Check your answers. If you write the date and get 100% you get a 2 second bonus!

Medals & Prizes!

Make Antonio by setting a Personal Best, reaching your goal, and winning a medal.

- ANT — 20
- Gold — 30
- Silver — 50
- Bronze — 1:30

Hand Speed Bonus

Total Time

ANTONIO

P * B   GOAL

Question	A		B		C
1	3	+	5	=	x
2	0	+	8	=	x
3	2	+	4	=	x
4	0	+	5	=	x
5	5	+	5	=	x
6	2	+	7	=	x
7	3	+	4	=	x
8	1	+	3	=	x
9	5	+	4	=	x
10	3	+	3	=	x

copyright ant.london

| Ex. | 28 | Number Bonds To Ten - Medley | Date |

Circle your goal. Fill in the numbers iin the boxes marked 'X'. Check your answers. If you write the date and get 100% you get a 2 second bonus!

Question	A		B		C	Medals & Prizes!	
1	x	+	8	=	10	Make Antonio by setting a Personal Best, reaching your goal, and winning a medal.	
2	8	+	x	=	10	20	ANT
3	1	+	5	=	x	30	Gold
4	4	+	x	=	10	50	Silver
5	x	+	8	=	10	1:30	Bronze
6	8	+	x	=	10	Hand Speed Bonus	
7	2	+	3	=	x	Total Time	
8	10	+	x	=	10	ANTONIO	
9	x	+	1	=	10	P * B	GOAL
10	8	+	x	=	10		

copyright ant.london

Date	Number Bonds To Ten - A Type	Ex.	29

Circle your goal. Fill in the numbers in the 'A' Column. If you write the date and get 100% you get a 2 second bonus!

Medals & Prizes!

Make Antonio by setting a Personal Best, reaching your goal, and winning a medal.

ANT	20
Gold	30
Silver	50
Bronze	1:30
Hand Speed	
Bonus	
Total Time	

ANTONIO

P * B   GOAL

Question	A		B		C
1	x	+	7	=	10
2	x	+	5	=	10
3	x	+	2	=	10
4	x	+	6	=	10
5	x	+	5	=	10
6	x	+	5	=	10
7	x	+	9	=	10
8	x	+	4	=	10
9	x	+	7	=	10
10	x	+	9	=	10

copyright ant.london

Ex.	30	Number Bonds To Ten - B Type	Date

Circle your goal. Fill in the numbers in the 'B' Column. If you write the date and get 100% you get a 2 second bonus!

Question	A		B		C	Medals & Prizes!	
1	1	+		=	10		
2	1	+		=	10	20	ANT
3	3	+		=	10	30	Gold
4	5	+		=	10	50	Silver
5	1	+		=	10	1:30	Bronze
6	7	+		=	10		Hand Speed Bonus
7	0	+		=	10		Total Time
8	0	+		=	10		
9	10	+		=	10		
10	1	+		=	10		

Make Antonio by setting a Personal Best, reaching your goal, and winning a medal.

ANTONIO

P * B   GOAL

Date	Number Bonds To Ten - C Type	Ex	31

Circle your goal. Fill in the numbers in the 'C' Column. Check your answers. If you write the date and get 100% you get a 2 second bonus!

Medals & Prizes!

Make Antonio by setting a Personal Best, reaching your goal, and winning a medal.

ANT	20
Gold	30
Silver	50
Bronze	1:30

Hand Speed

Bonus

Total Time

ANTONIO

P * B   GOAL

Question	A		B		C
1	5	+	3	=	x
2	1	+	8	=	x
3	2	+	2	=	x
4	5	+	1	=	x
5	3	+	4	=	x
6	3	+	5	=	x
7	1	+	5	=	x
8	3	+	1	=	x
9	5	+	2	=	x
10	0	+	0	=	x

copyright ant.london

| Ex. | 32 | Number Bonds To Ten - Medley | Date |

Circle your goal. Fill in the numbers in the boxes marked 'X'. Check your answers. If you write the date and get 100% you get a 2 second bonus!

Question	A		B		C
1	X	+	1	=	10
2	0	+	X	=	10
3	5	+	2	=	X
4	8	+	X	=	10
5	X	+	6	=	10
6	3	+	X	=	10
7	4	+	5	=	X
8	4	+	X	=	10
9	X	+	7	=	10
10	5	+	X	=	10

Medals & Prizes!

Make Antonio by setting a Personal Best, reaching your goal, and winning a medal.

20	ANT
30	Gold
50	Silver
1:30	Bronze

Hand Speed Bonus

Total Time

ANTONIO
P * B   GOAL

| Date (to qualify for bonus) | Number Bonds To Ten - A Type | Ex. | 33 |

Circle your goal. Fill in the numbers in the 'A' Column. If you write the date and get 100% you get a 2 second bonus!

Medals & Prizes!		Question	A		B		C
Make Antonio by setting a Personal Best, reaching your goal, and winning a medal.							
ANT	20	1	x	+	5	=	10
Gold	30	2	x	+	7	=	10
Silver	50	3	x	+	5	=	10
Bronze	1:30	4	x	+	3	=	10
Hand Speed		5	x	+	10	=	10
Bonus		6	x	+	0	=	10
Total Time		7	x	+	0	=	10

ANTONIO

P * B   GOAL

8	x	+	8	=	10
9	x	+	1	=	10
10	x	+	8	=	10

copyright ant.london

Ex.	34	Number Bonds To Ten - B Type	Date

Circle your goal. Fill in the numbers in the 'B' Column. If you write the date and get 100% you get a 2 second bonus!

Question	A		B		C	Medals & Prizes!	
1	4	+	x	=	10		
2	2	+	x	=	10	20	ANT
3	9	+	x	=	10	30	Gold
4	7	+	x	=	10	50	Silver
5	3	+	x	=	10	1:30	Bronze
6	6	+	x	=	10	Hand Speed	
7	0	+	x	=	10	Bonus / Total Time	
8	10	+	x	=	10	ANTONIO P*B / GOAL	
9	9	+	x	=	10		
10	8	+	x	=	10		

| | | Date | | Number Bonds To Ten - C Type | | | | Ex | 35 |

Circle your goal. Fill in the numbers in the 'C' Column. Check your answers. If you write the date and get 100% you get a 2 second bonus!

Medals & Prizes!

Make Antonio by setting a Personal Best, reaching your goal, and winning a medal.

Medal	Time
ANT	20
Gold	30
Silver	50
Bronze	1:30

Hand Speed
Bonus
Total Time

ANTONIO
P * B   GOAL

Question	A		B		C
1	5	+	2	=	x
2	0	+	8	=	x
3	3	+	5	=	x
4	0	+	2	=	x
5	2	+	2	=	x
6	3	+	6	=	x
7	2	+	4	=	x
8	3	+	0	=	x
9	2	+	5	=	x
10	5	+	5	=	x

copyright ant.london

| Ex. | 36 | Number Bonds To Ten - Medley | Date |

Circle your goal. Fill in the numbers iin the boxes marked 'X'. Check your answers. If you write the date and get 100% you get a 2 second bonus!

Question	A		B		C	Medals & Prizes!
1	X	+	1	=	10	Make Antonio by setting a Personal Best, reaching your goal, and winning a medal.
2	9	+	X	=	10	20 — ANT
3	4	+	4	=	X	30 — Gold
4	7	+	X	=	10	50 — Silver
5	X	+	5	=	10	1:30 — Bronze
6	5	+	X	=	10	Hand Speed
7	0	+	0	=	X	Bonus / Total Time
8	4	+	X	=	10	ANTONIO — P * B — GOAL
9	X	+	0	=	10	
10	7	+	X	=	10	

ant.london

Number Bonds To Ten - A Type   Ex. 37

Circle your goal. Fill in the numbers in the 'A' Column. If you write the date and get 100% you get a 2 second bonus!

Medals & Prizes!

Make Antonio by setting a Personal Best, reaching your goal, and winning a medal.

Medal	Time
ANT	20
Gold	30
Silver	50
Bronze	1:30

Hand Speed

Bonus

Total Time

ANTONIO
P * B   GOAL

Question	A		B		C
1	x	+	2	=	10
2	x	+	4	=	10
3	x	+	10	=	10
4	x	+	4	=	10
5	x	+	3	=	10
6	x	+	2	=	10
7	x	+	1	=	10
8	x	+	10	=	10
9	x	+	0	=	10
10	x	+	7	=	10

copyright ant.london

Ex.	38	Number Bonds To Ten - B Type	Date

Circle your goal. Fill in the numbers in the 'B' Column. If you write the date and get 100% you get a 2 second bonus!

Question	A		B		C	Medals & Prizes!	
1	1	+		=	10		
2	9	+		=	10	20	ANT
3	6	+		=	10	30	Gold
4	2	+		=	10	50	Silver
5	8	+		=	10	1:30	Bronze
6	10	+		=	10	Hand Speed	
7	1	+		=	10	Bonus / Total Time	
8	1	+		=	10	ANTONIO P*B / GOAL	
9	0	+		=	10		
10	5	+		=	10		

copyright ant.london

Date	Number Bonds To Ten - C Type	Ex	39

Circle your goal. Fill in the numbers in the 'C' Column. Check your answers. If you write the date and get 100% you get a 2 second bonus!

Medals & Prizes!

Make Antonio by setting a Personal Best, reaching your goal, and winning a medal.

- ANT — 20
- Gold — 30
- Silver — 50
- Bronze — 1:30

Hand Speed

Bonus

Total Time

ANTONIO

P * B   GOAL

Question	A		B		C
1	4	+	2	=	x
2	1	+	8	=	x
3	2	+	4	=	x
4	5	+	4	=	x
5	2	+	5	=	x
6	2	+	7	=	x
7	2	+	1	=	x
8	2	+	5	=	x
9	3	+	4	=	x
10	5	+	0	=	x

copyright ant.london

| Ex. | 40 | Number Bonds To Ten - Medley | Date |

Circle your goal. Fill in the numbers in the boxes marked 'X'. Check your answers. If you write the date and get 100% you get a 2 second bonus!

Question	A		B		C	Medals & Prizes!
1	X	+	5	=	10	Make Antonio by setting a Personal Best, reaching your goal, and winning a medal.
2	8	+	X	=	10	20 — ANT
3	1	+	5	=	X	30 — Gold
4	6	+	X	=	10	50 — Silver
5	X	+	5	=	10	1:30 — Bronze
6	7	+	X	=	10	Hand Speed / Bonus
7	3	+	3	=	X	Total Time
8	3	+	X	=	10	ANTONIO — P * B — GOAL
9	X	+	0	=	10	
10	4	+	X	=	10	

copyright ant.london

ANT Maths - Performance Graph - Set

Zone	Seconds
ANT Zone	15–20
Gold Zone	21–30
Silver Zone	31–50
Bronze Zone	51–90
Growth Zone	91–110

Ex. 21 → Ex. 22 → Ex. 23 → Ex. 24 → Ex. 25 → Ex. 26 → Ex. 27 → Ex. 28 → Ex. 29 → Ex. 30 →

Date

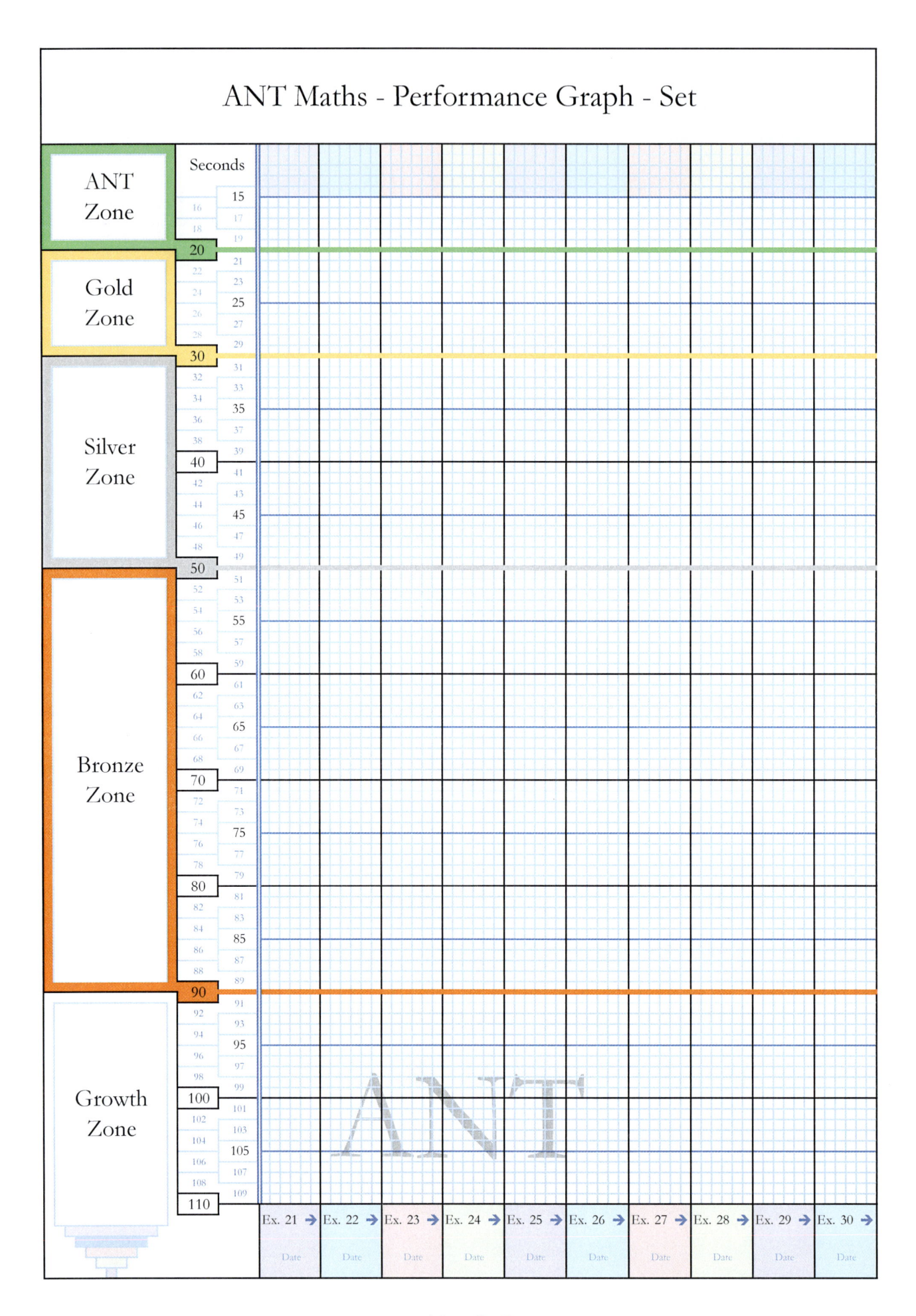

copyright ant.london

Plot the graph according to exercise type. A Type to A Type, B Type to B Type, C Type to C Type, Medley to Medley. Draw the lines using the colours in the boxes. This way you can tell which type your brain finds easiest - and work towards creating a balanced brain that will work equally easily in any direction.

Seconds	Zone
15, 16, 17, 18, 19, 20	ANT Zone
21, 22, 23, 24, 25, 26, 27, 28, 29, 30	Gold Zone
31, 32, 33, 34, 35, 36, 37, 38, 39, 40, 41, 42, 43, 44, 45, 46, 47, 48, 49, 50	Silver Zone
51, 52, 53, 54, 55, 56, 57, 58, 59, 60, 61, 62, 63, 64, 65, 66, 67, 68, 69, 70, 71, 72, 73, 74, 75, 76, 77, 78, 79, 80, 81, 82, 83, 84, 85, 86, 87, 88, 89, 90	Bronze Zone
91, 92, 93, 94, 95, 96, 97, 98, 99, 100, 101, 102, 103, 104, 105, 106, 107, 108, 109, 110	Growth Zone

Ex. 31 → Ex. 32 → Ex. 33 → Ex. 34 → Ex. 35 → Ex. 36 → Ex. 37 → Ex. 38 → Ex. 39 → Ex. 40 →

Date   Date   Date   Date   Date   Date   Date   Date   Date   Date

copyright ant.london

ANT Maths - Performance Graph - Set

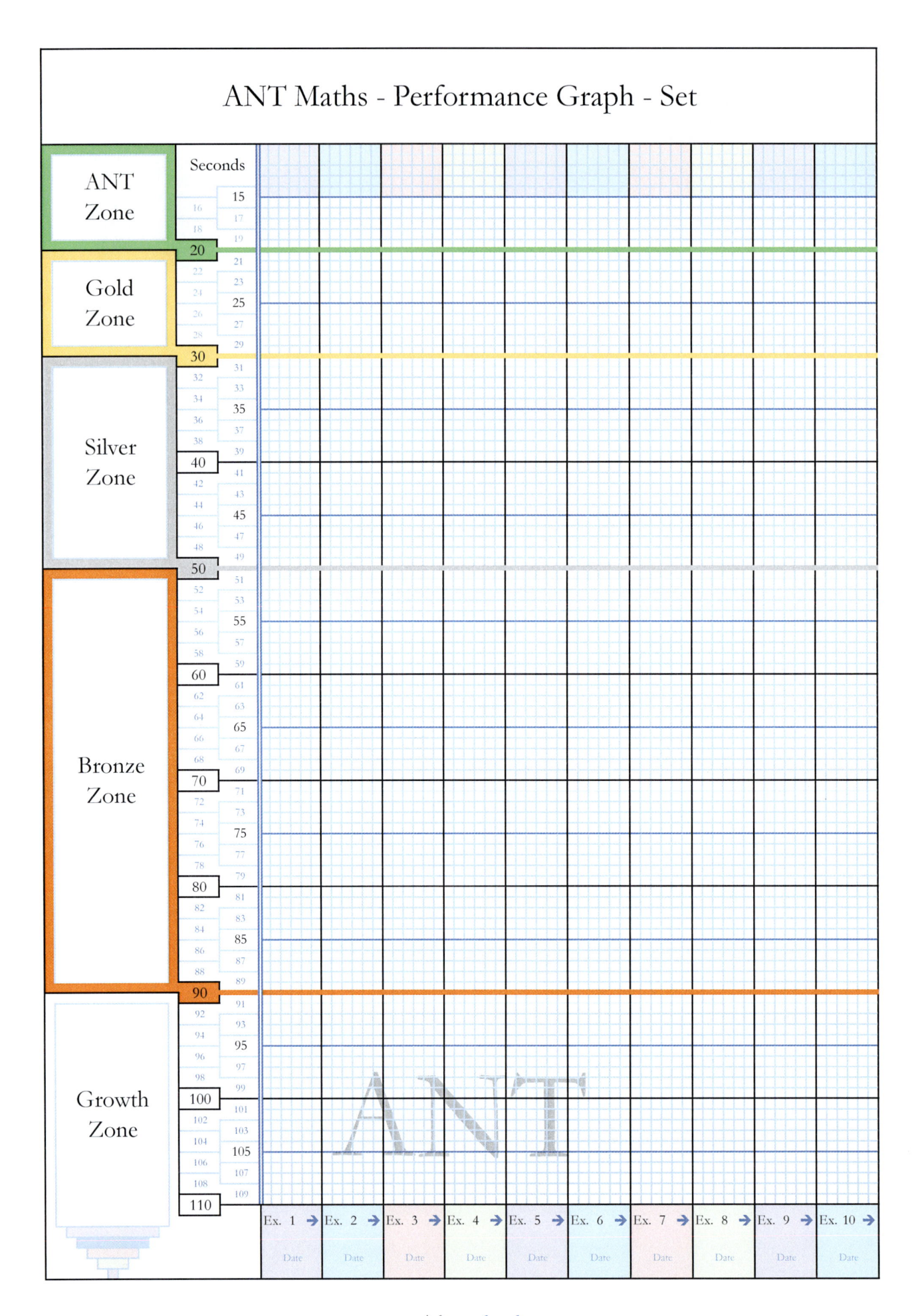

Zone	Seconds
ANT Zone	15, 16, 17, 18, 19, 20
Gold Zone	21, 22, 23, 24, 25, 26, 27, 28, 29, 30
Silver Zone	31, 32, 33, 34, 35, 36, 37, 38, 39, 40, 41, 42, 43, 44, 45, 46, 47, 48, 49, 50
Bronze Zone	51, 52, 53, 54, 55, 56, 57, 58, 59, 60, 61, 62, 63, 64, 65, 66, 67, 68, 69, 70, 71, 72, 73, 74, 75, 76, 77, 78, 79, 80, 81, 82, 83, 84, 85, 86, 87, 88, 89, 90
Growth Zone	91, 92, 93, 94, 95, 96, 97, 98, 99, 100, 101, 102, 103, 104, 105, 106, 107, 108, 109, 110

Ex. 1 → Ex. 2 → Ex. 3 → Ex. 4 → Ex. 5 → Ex. 6 → Ex. 7 → Ex. 8 → Ex. 9 → Ex. 10 →

Date

copyright ant.london

Plot the graph according to exercise type. A Type to A Type, B Type to B Type, C Type to C Type, Medley to Medley. Draw the lines using the colours in the boxes. This way you can tell which type your brain finds easiest - and work towards creating a balanced brain that will work equally easily in any direction.

Seconds	Zone
15–19	ANT Zone
20–29	Gold Zone
30–49	Silver Zone
50–89	Bronze Zone
90–110	Growth Zone

Ex. 11 → Ex. 12 → Ex. 13 → Ex. 14 → Ex. 15 → Ex. 16 → Ex. 17 → Ex. 18 → Ex. 19 → Ex. 20 →

Date | Date | Date | Date | Date | Date | Date | Date | Date | Date

copyright ant.london

Animate Antonio

If you medalled in every category, you can colour in a section of Antonio for that question type.

A

B

C

D

copyright ant.london